Contents

*C = copper; B = bronze; S = silver; ( ) = the line must be played but cannot be assessed for a Medal.

Levels in bold type indicate that the piece is for mixed saxophones. In each of these cases, the instrumentation is given at the start of the piece. Every other piece can be played either on E flat saxophones or on B flat saxophones.

Where Seagulls Dare

James Rae

AB 3139

Lady Bay Bridge

Andy Hampton

Angles

Colin Cowles

Lazy Saturday

Chris Allen

Minuet

from *Music for the Royal Fireworks*

Handel arr. Mark Goddard

AB 3139

Lonely Romeo

Gordon Lewin

One Shoe Off

Andrew Wilson

AB 3139

Marche Pastorale

James Rae

Queue Jumping!

Paul Harris

AB 3139

Strollin'

Mark Lockheart

AB 3139

Invincible March

James Rae

Con moto ♩ = *c.*124

AB 3139

Saxomarch

John Reynolds

AB 3139

Blue Train

Sarah Watts

Star Light…Neon Light

Paul Harris

AB 3139

Lento espressivo

rall.

Jump To It!

Michael Rose

AB 3139

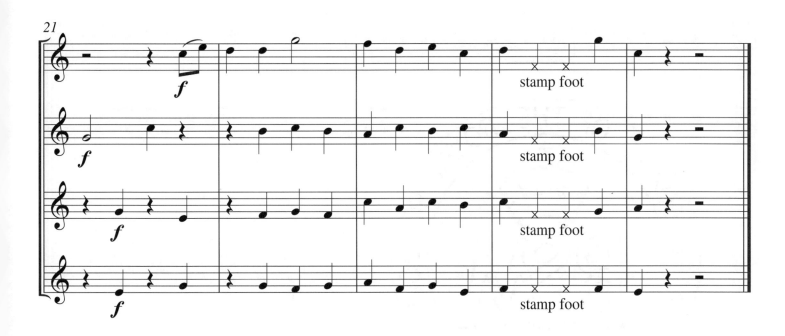

A Funfair Fanfare

Colin Cowles

Come What May
(from 'Moulin Rouge')

Words & Music by David Baerwald

Tenderly ♩ = 66

9

Angie

Words & Music by Mick Jagger & Keith Richards

Blueberry Hill

Words & Music by Larry Stock, Al Lewis & Vincent Rose

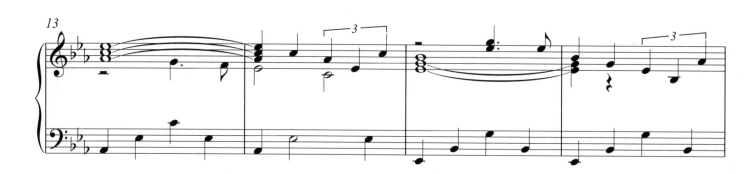

12

Canon In D

Music by Johann Pachelbel

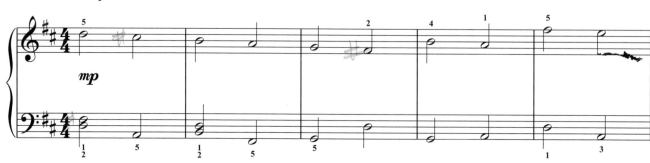

14

Chasing Cars

Words & Music by Paul Wilson, Gary Lightbody,
Jonathan Quinn, Nathan Connolly & Tom Simpson

Moderately ♩ = 104

Crazy

Words & Music by Willie Nelson

18

Dancing Queen

Words & Music by Benny Andersson, Stig Anderson & Björn Ulvaeus

Strong rock ♩ = 120

Don't Know Why

Words & Music by Jesse Harris

24

D.S. al Coda   ⊕ **Coda**

The Entertainer

Music by Scott Joplin

Feather Theme
(Main Title from the film 'Forrest Gump')

Music by Alan Silvestri

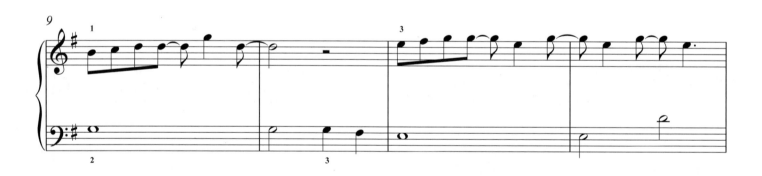

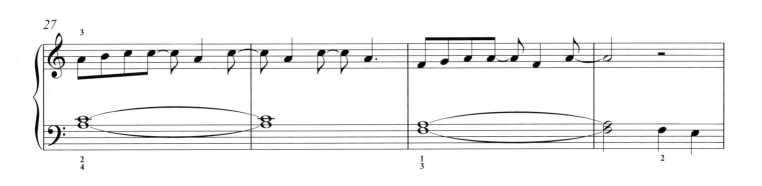

Fragile

Words & Music by Sting

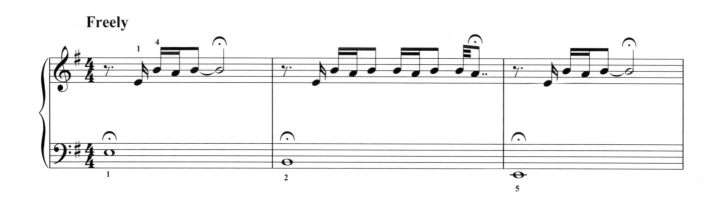

33

To Coda ⊕

D.S. al Coda

Coda

Freely

Für Elise

Music by Ludwig Van Beethoven

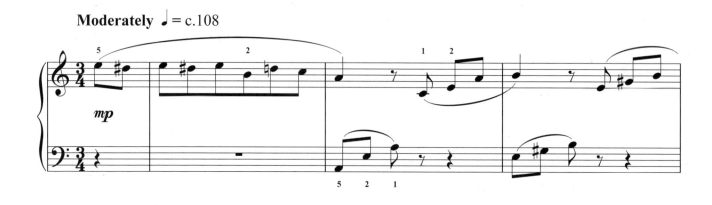

36

The Girl From Ipanema
('Garota De Ipanema')

Music by Antonio Carlos Jobim, Original Words by Vinicius De Moraes,
English Words by Norman Gimbel

Bossa nova ♩ = 116

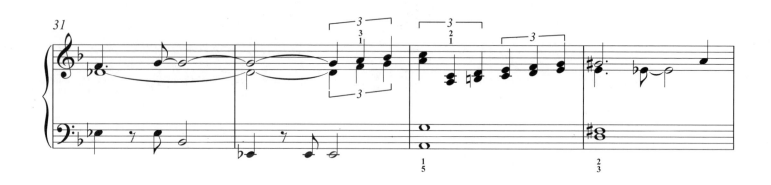

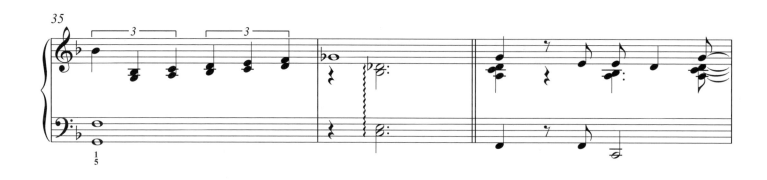

rall.

Going Home
(Theme from 'Local Hero')

Music by Mark Knopfler

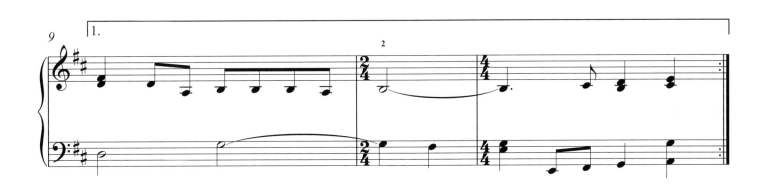

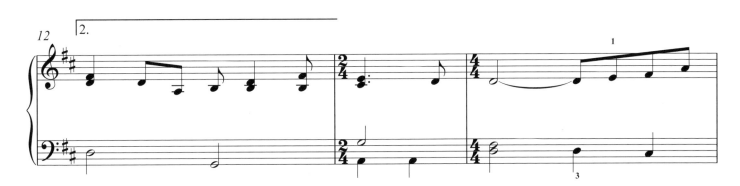

To Coda ⊕

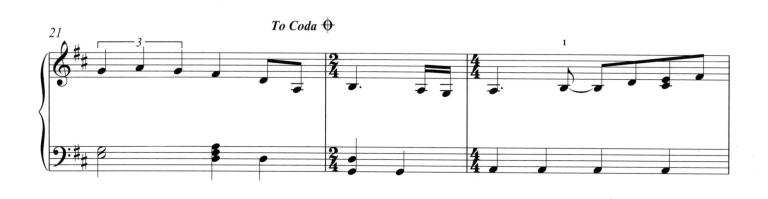

D.S. al Coda　　　　　⊕ **Coda**

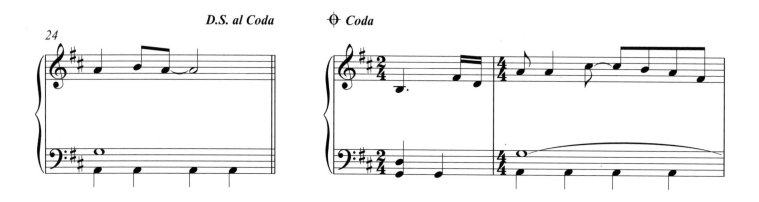

Glasgow Love Theme
(from 'Love Actually')

Music by Craig Armstrong

Slowly, very freely ♩ = c.58

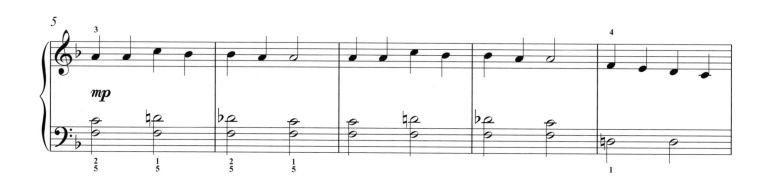

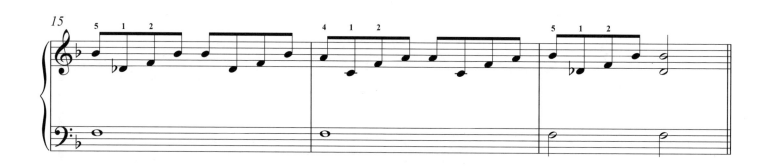

rit.

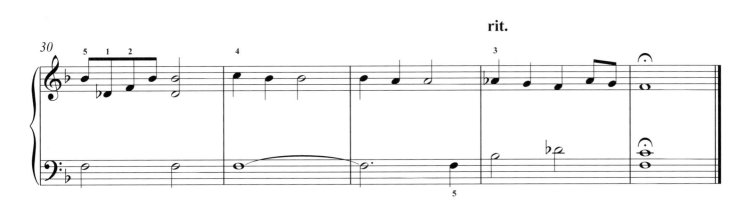

Half The World Away

Words & Music by Noel Gallagher

With a lilt ♩ = c.110

Have A Nice Day

Words & Music by Kelly Jones

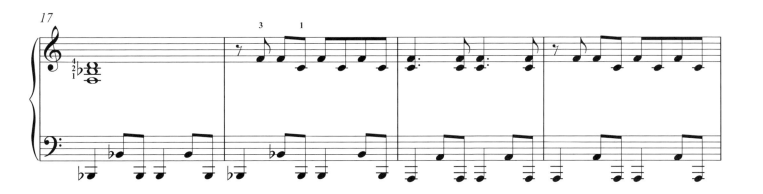

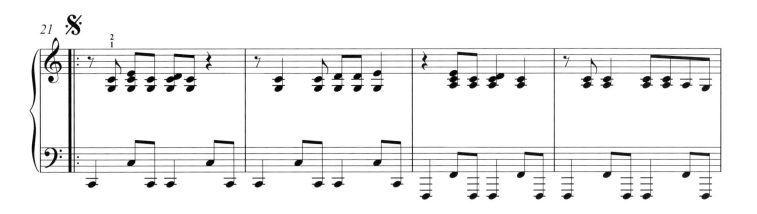

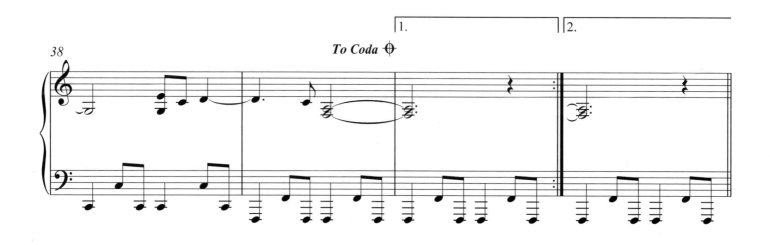

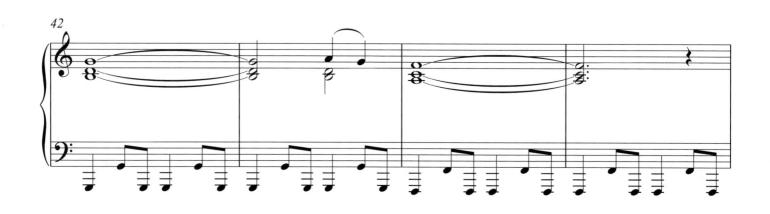

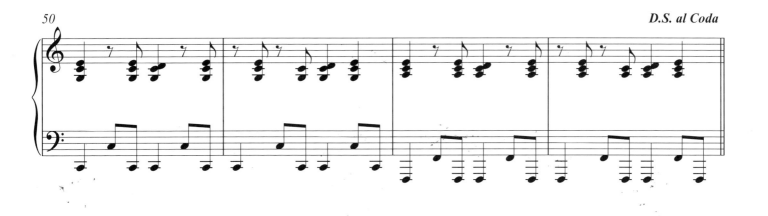

Coda

Repeat and fade

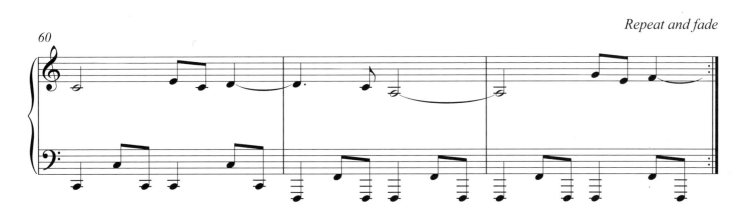

A Hazy Shade Of Winter

Words & Music by Paul Simon

Briskly ♩ = 132

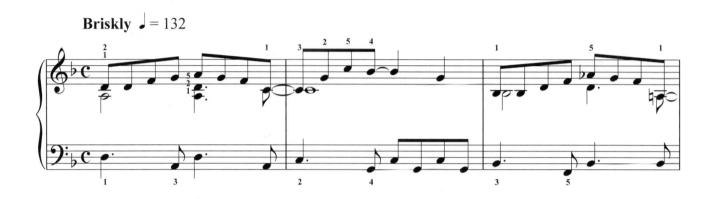

Hey, That's No Way To Say Goodbye

Words & Music by Leonard Cohen

Slow and flowing ♩ = c.76

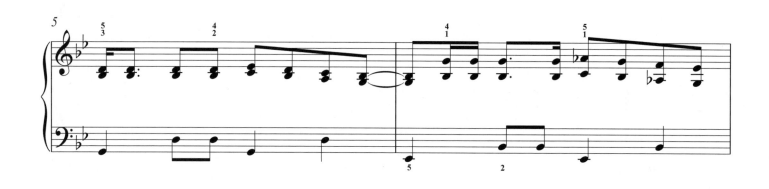

Hopelessly Devoted To You
(from 'Grease')

Words & Music by John Farrar

58

I Get The Sweetest Feeling

Words & Music by Van McCoy & Alicia Evelyn

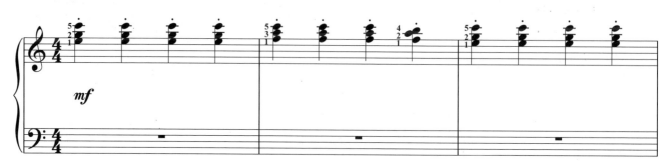

Knockin' On Heaven's Door

Words & Music by Bob Dylan

Slow Country Ballad ♩ = 67

I Wish I Knew How It Would Feel To Be Free

Words by Billy Taylor & Dick Dallas, Music by Billy Taylor

I'll Be Your Baby Tonight

Words & Music by Bob Dylan

Jealous Guy

Words & Music by John Lennon

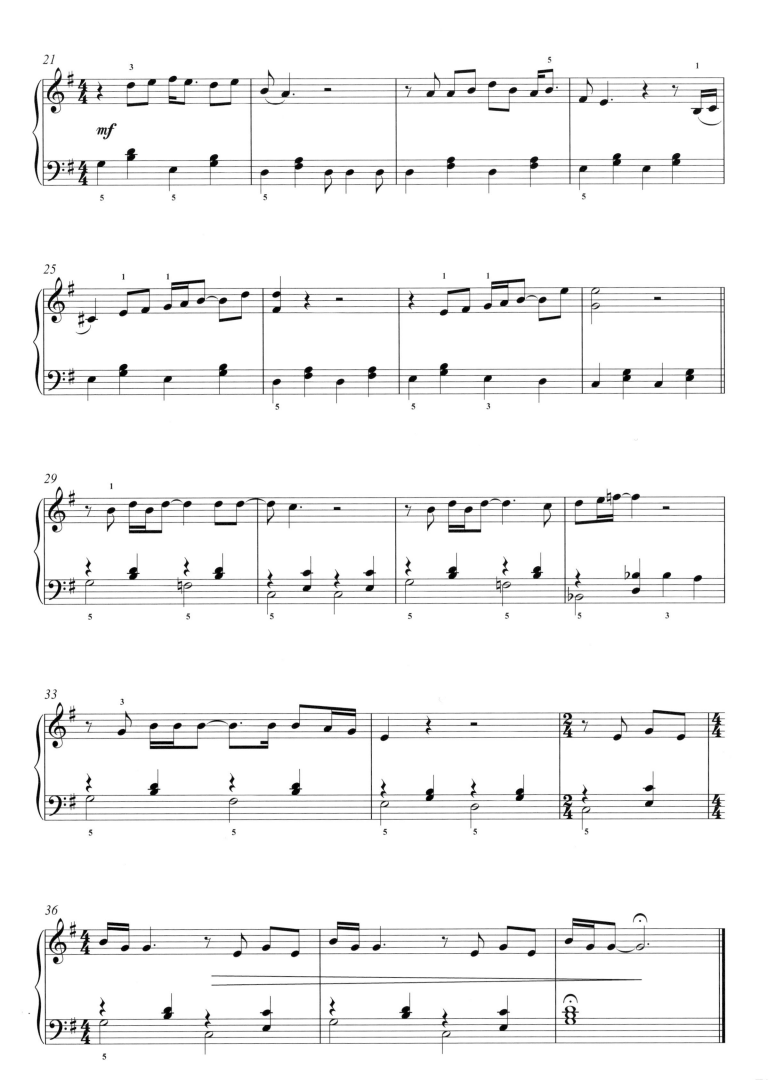

Jurassic Park
(Theme)

Music by John Williams

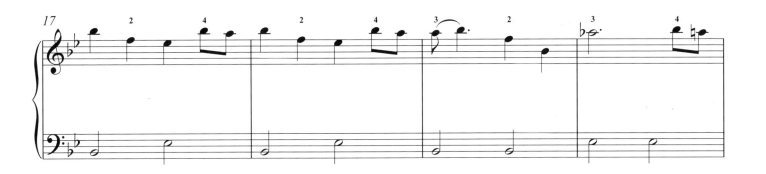

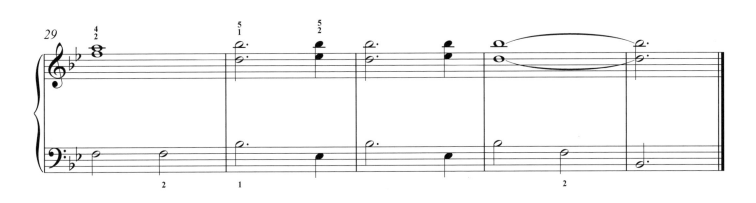

Life On Mars?

Words & Music by David Bowie

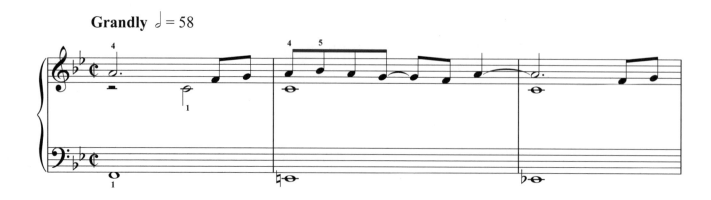

The Long And Winding Road

Words & Music by John Lennon & Paul McCartney

Expressively ♩ = c.63

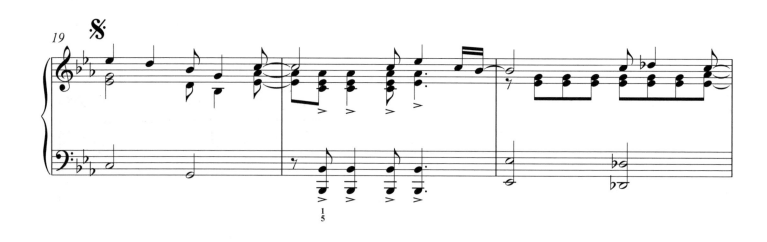

To Coda ⊕

D.S. al Coda

⊕ Coda

Maybe This Time
(from 'Cabaret')

Words by Fred Ebb, Music by John Kander

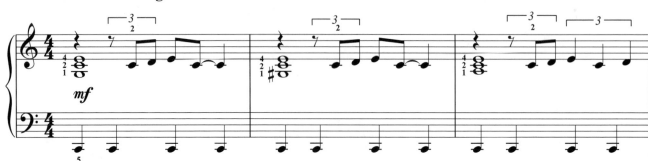

Moon River

Words by Johnny Mercer, Music by Henry Mancini

Lyrically ♩ = 84

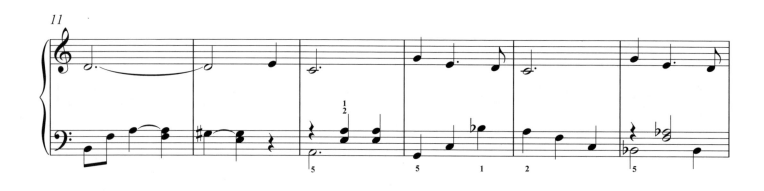

82

My Heart Will Go On
(Love Theme from 'Titanic')

Words by Will Jennings, Music by James Horner

Flowing ♩ = 96

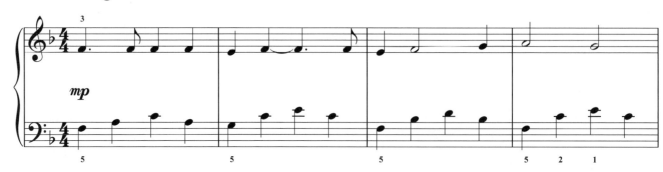

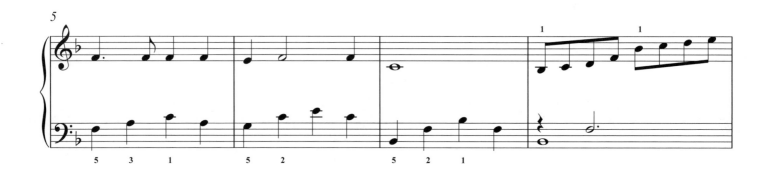

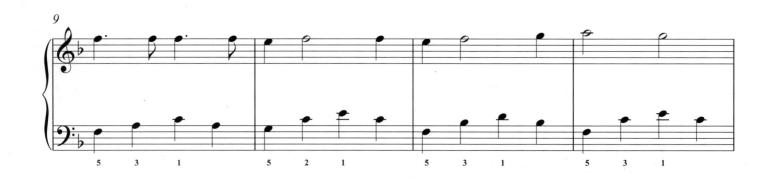

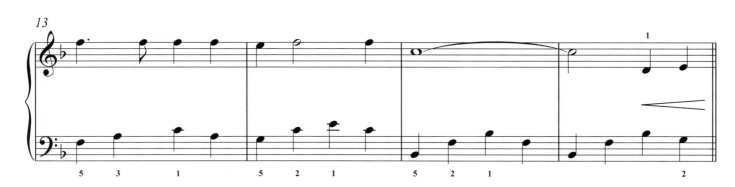

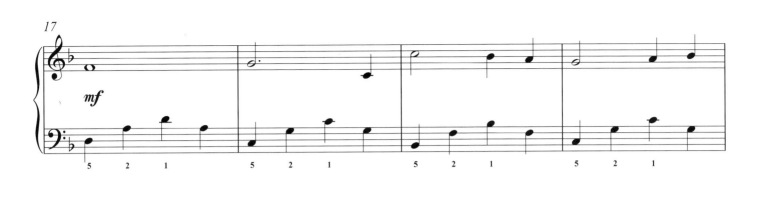

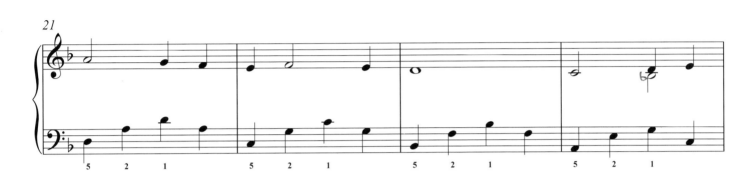

Nights In White Satin

Words & Music by Justin Hayward

Non Più Andrai
(from 'The Marriage Of Figaro')

Music by Wolfgang Amadeus Mozart

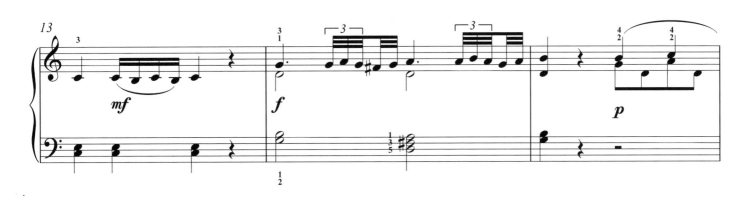

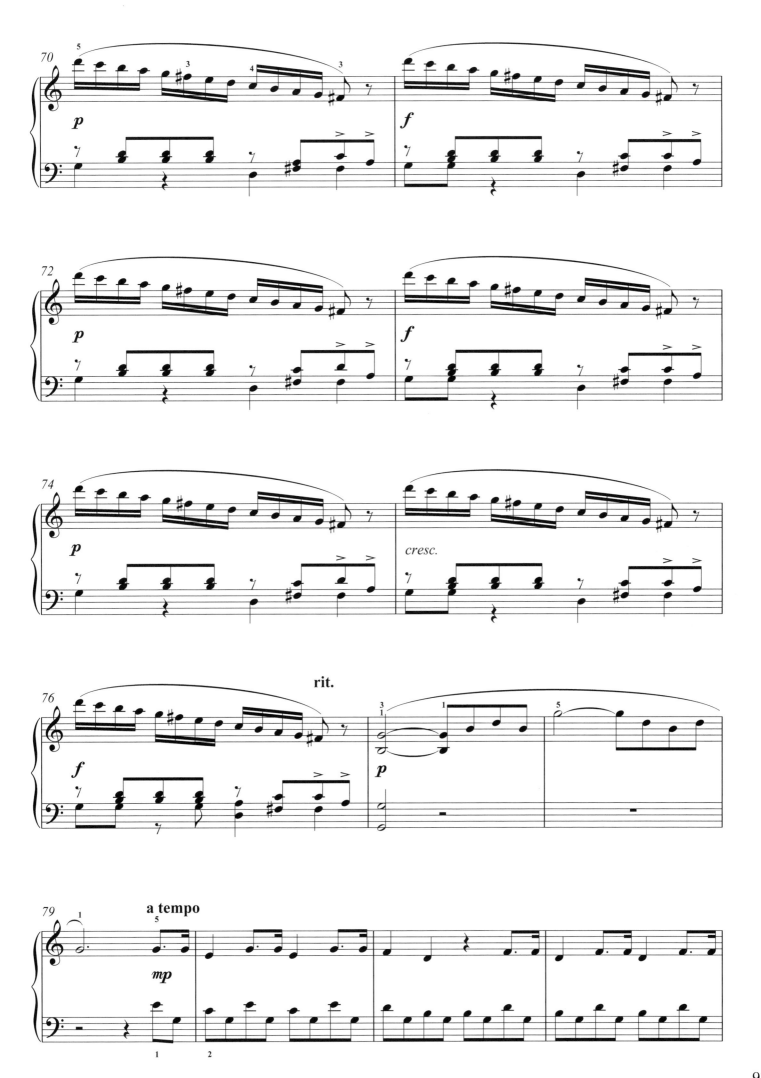

One

Words & Music by U2

Patience

Words & Music by Mark Owen, Gary Barlow, John Shanks, Jason Orange & Howard Donald

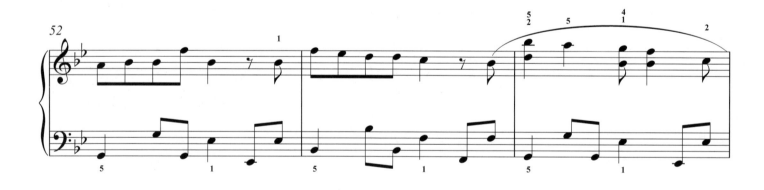

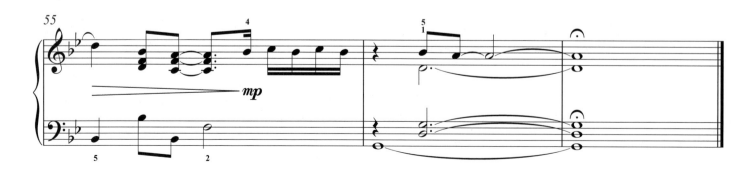

Prelude Op.28, No.15 'Raindrop'

Music by Frédéric Chopin

102

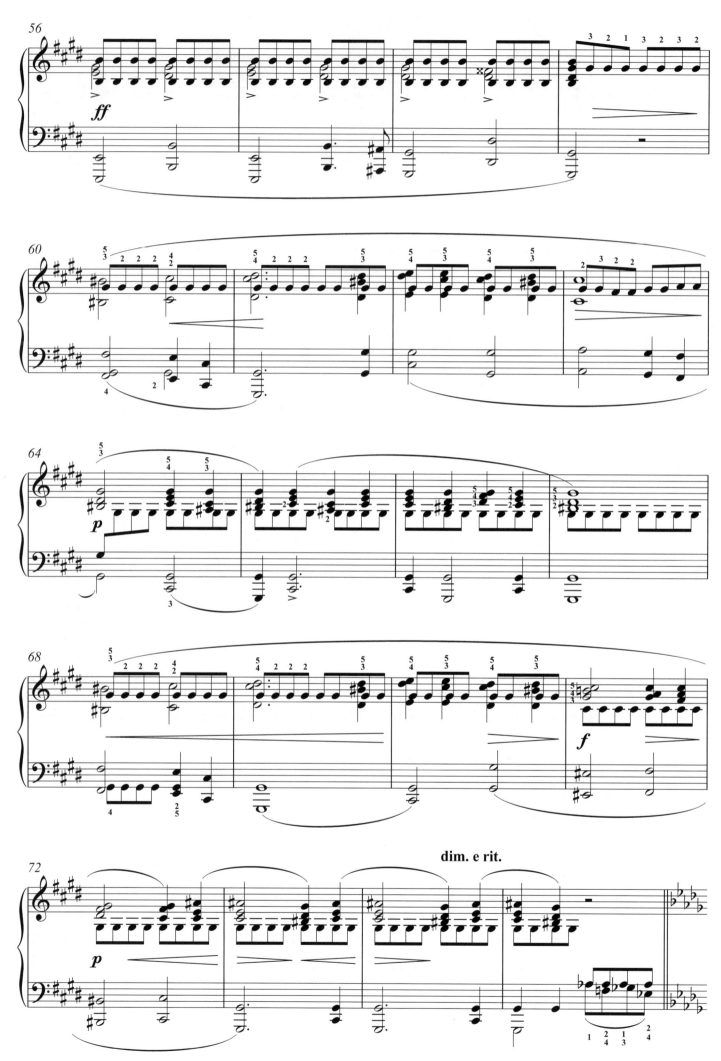

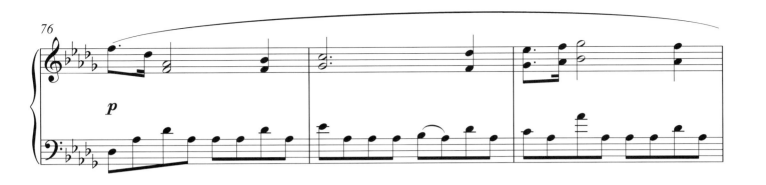

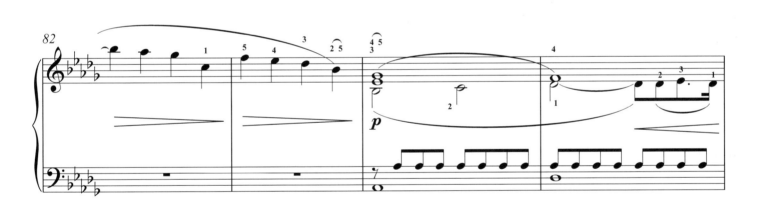

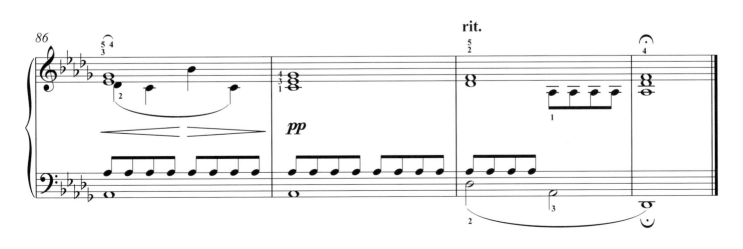

Pie Jesu
(from 'Requiem')

Music by Andrew Lloyd Webber

Sweetly ♩ = c.60

Theme From The Simpsons™

(from the Twentieth Century Fox television series 'The Simpsons')

Music by Danny Elfman

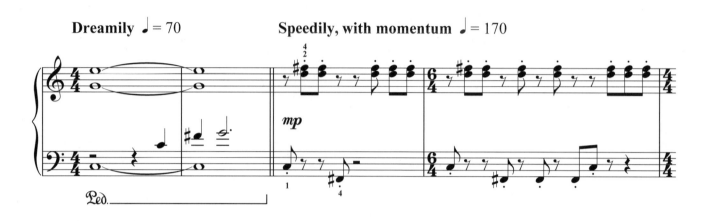

Heavy swing ♩ = 110

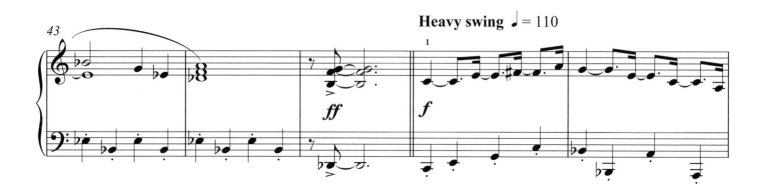

Straight quavers

Speedily ♩ = 170

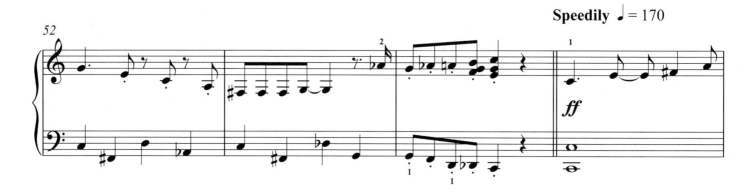

110

Somethin' Stupid

Words & Music by C. Carson Parks

Relaxed ♩ = 104

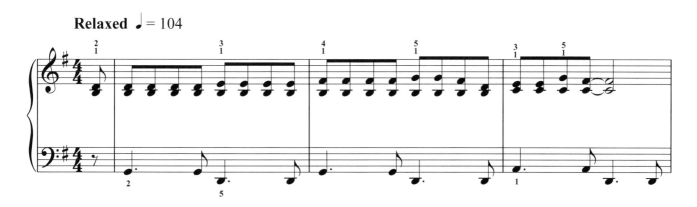

Song For Guy

Music by Elton John

Moderately ♩ = c.104

Take Five

Music by Paul Desmond

Moderately fast ♩ = 176

117

119

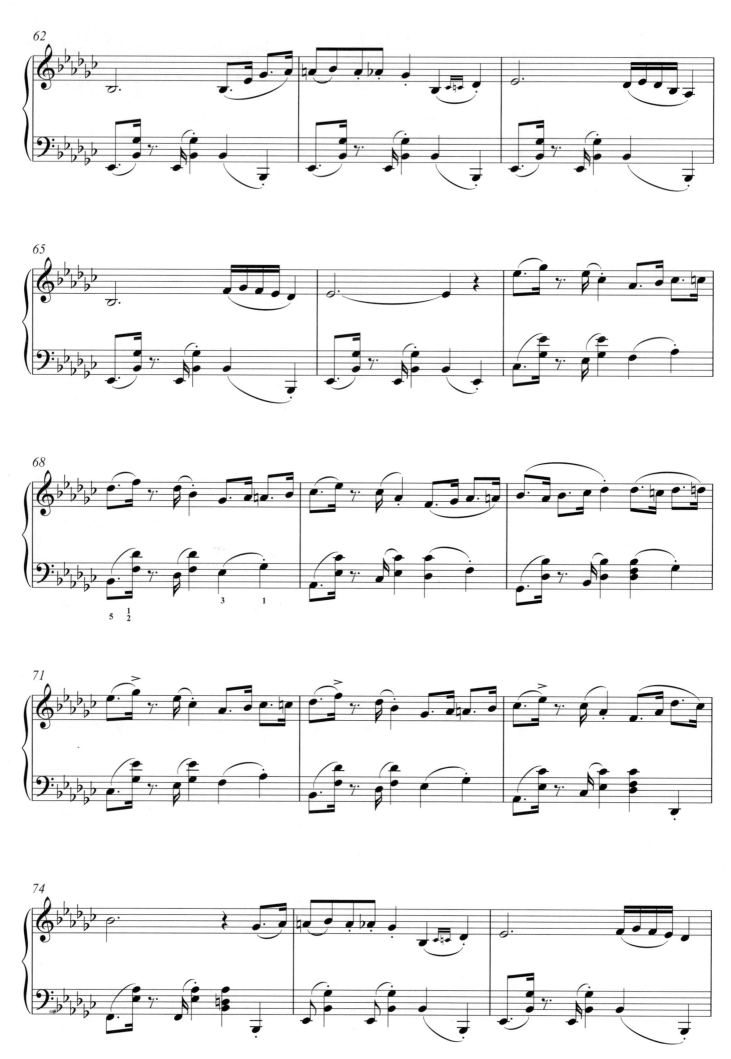

120

Take The 'A' Train

Words & Music by Billy Strayhorn

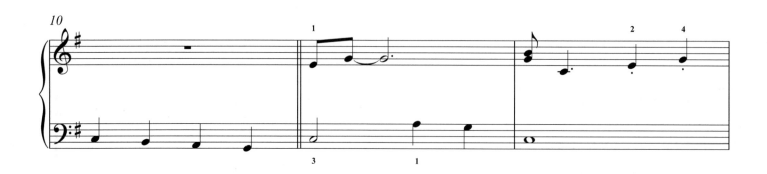

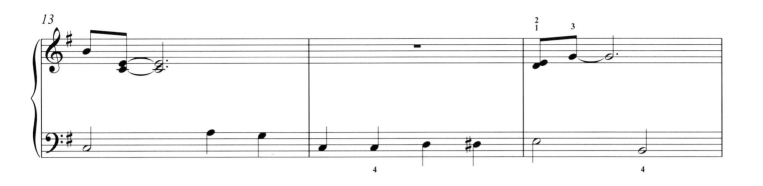

Time To Say Goodbye
('Con Te Partirò')

Words by Lucio Quarantotto & Frank Peterson, Music by Francesco Sartori

Trouble

Words & Music by Guy Berryman, Chris Martin, Jon Buckland & Will Champion

Moderately slow ♩ = 66

Twin Peaks
(Theme)

Music by Angelo Badalamenti & David Lynch

Slowly and expressively ♩ = 82

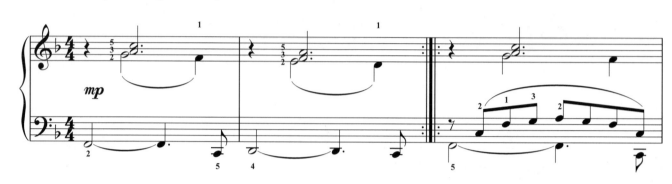

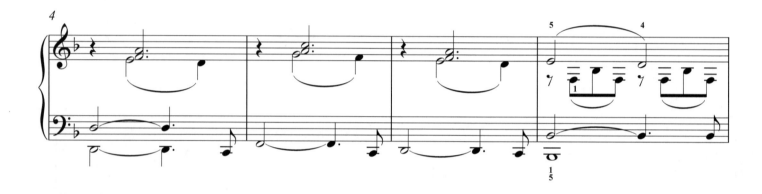

Repeat and fade

Warwick Avenue

Words & Music by Duffy, James Hogarth & Eg White

D.S. al Coda

Coda

134

Unchained Melody

Words by Hy Zaret, Music by Alex North

Slow and tenderly ♩ = c.54

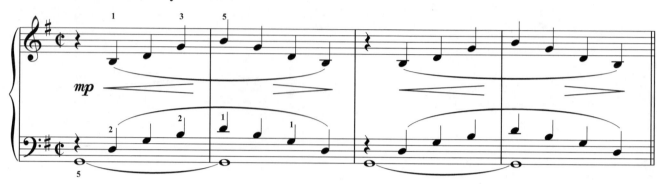

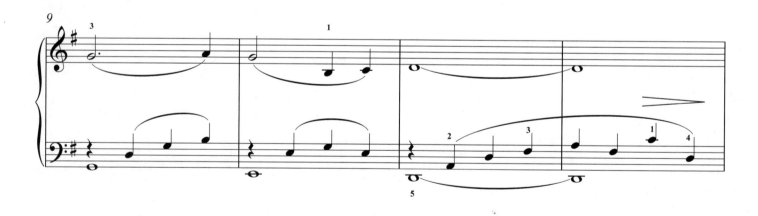

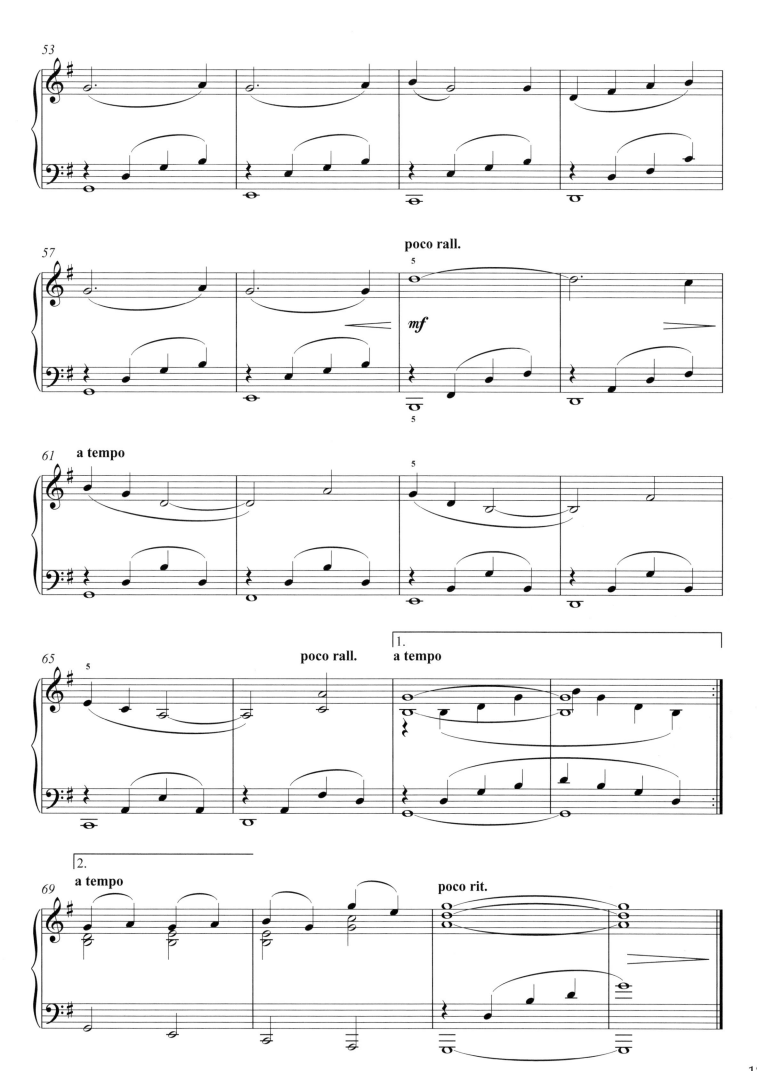

What A Wonderful World

Words & Music by George Weiss & Bob Thiele

Wild World

Words & Music by Cat Stevens

Steadily ♩ = 72

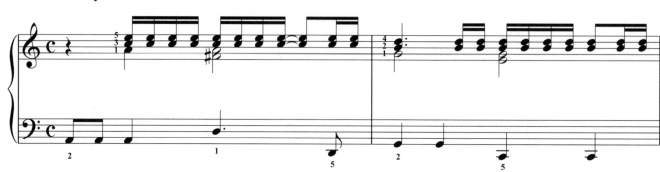

D.S. al Coda   ⊕ Coda

23456789

2/10 (173244)